This is not a Jewish story, although Moses is mentioned.
This is not a Muslim story, although Mohammed appears.
It is not a Buddhist story, although Buddha smiles in it.
It is not a Christian story, yet Jesus is one of its stars.
Nor is this book a science text,
though you'll hear the "big bang" discussed,
as well as genesis of how Nature came to be.

This is a story of one possible reason why...
though we all come from different places,
and all have different faces...
the one drummer that beats in every heart really is the same.

This story honors the One behind the many,
the unity behind our diversity.

A little story
about the biggest thing that ever happened

Story by Will Dalton
Illustrated by Lisa Kaiser

There was once a beautiful being who sat alone in the middle of the universe. So radiant, the purest white light glowed about her always. She was breath-taking. She was divine. All the twinkling stars revered her as their creator. She knew everything, remembered everything. She was complete intelligence. She had never been born and never died. Her imagination was so exceptional that anything she desired could be created in an instant.

For millions upon millions of years she quietly kept her own company. For billions upon billions of years, she sat and thought. For trillions upon trillions of years she endured her solitude until finally, she grew bored.

She yearned to be with another,

yet there was no other. She desired to give and to share, but there was nothing to which she could give and share. She wanted to nurture and caress, to hold and be held, appreciate and be appreciated, she wanted to play, to sing, to dance; she wanted to love.

Many aeons went by, and she became fed up. She knew herself to be joyous and was not pleased with her less than happy state. Because she could do anything and create anything, she spent her days thinking up solutions to her dilemma. One day she thought, "If I could see myself, then at least I would appreciate myself." Then, suddenly, out of nowhere, a mirror appeared, a mirror as big as the universe.

She was delighted in what she saw

and appreciated herself very much. Despite this, after one week, she was bored again. "I will need to think of something more elaborate", she thought "I don't want to just look at myself, I wish I could be with another being" And because her imagination was so powerful, in an instant she divided herself into two equal parts. She looked at the other being, an exact replica of herself, and was so delighted with her creation that she wept with joy. She could see and touch and play with her other self. They could even sing and dance together. But despite her new friend, in only a month, she began to feel bored again.

It was true that her new creation was better than any mirror. She could cuddle, kiss and caress! Yet her other self knew what she was thinking as she thought it, knew what she was to say before she said it, and even laughed at her jokes before she told them. This was not enough. Something more complex was in order. Something brilliant!

She needed to create a being

that was she and not she at the same time. She had to create something complex, magnificent, and extraordinary. Ages and eons went by. Then an idea began to bubble around her boundless mind. She thought, "If I could separate myself into a billion pieces and lose my memory, then when I met myself, it would be like meeting myself for the first time."

She pondered,

"I could make so many parts of me that I would never get bored. I could create the impression of a beginning and an end, a start and a finish. I could design my senses to seek outwardly, yet I shall reside inwardly. I shall create a place, a playground, a world so beautifully delightful that upon my arrival, I will almost mistake its wonders for being more satisfying than the delight of knowing myself."

She giggled with pleasure at her own ingenuity. "I shall then be walking around, magnificent, powerful, yet forgetful. I will never find myself, so I will never be bored again!" After napping on her idea for an eon or two she awoke from her slumber and concluded that her thoughts from the previous epoch were extreme.

If she created her new idea,

she'd be eternally trapped in a world of forgetfulness. She would never find herself, and that would be even more lonely, even more unexciting. Plus, she knew in all truth that the discovery of herself would be the greatest gift of all. "I will make some refinements, some minor adjustments." she thought. "I shall give myself some little clues, so that if I'm listening carefully I will lead myself right back to me." Satisfied with her solution, she adjusted the volume of the world to be more colorful and slightly louder than the allure of herself. Then, smiling softly and compassionately, the ultimate creation streamed forth from her intensely focused imagination. She spared nothing in her conception. Nothing!

Her idea hurtled though space,
building up speed and magnificence and in an instant,
in a moment, in a sound, a clap, a bang, a very big bang,
God separated herself.

BANG!

In that moment,

endless universes were created, gases, stars, planets, suns, moons, oceans, plant life, animals, and human beings. She was pleased, but now was not able to know the depth of her pleasure because she had been successful; she had forgotten that she was God.

The humans that embodied her

arrived even better than expected. They had five of their
six senses looking toward the world and only one sense,
the sixth sense turned toward her inner self. The humans
were exactly as she had planned: perfect, magnificent,
beautiful, and completely forgetful.

Every part of her was encoded in the humans,

including God's incredible imagination, which could instantly create anything it thought into physical form. So successful was God in forgetting, that it took ages and eons for humans to create things that they wanted. So effective was her plan of not recognizing her self, some parts of herself waged war against other parts. It seemed that these fragments of God, humans mostly, were so infatuated with the world that they would fight each other to own it. This made God sad, which of course made every warring person sad. "Perhaps I made the allure of the world too strong and my attraction too weak," God thought, because only a handful of people were hearing the beckoning of God's magnificent kingdom. Centuries passed, the world evolved, and still the humans were overly forgetful. Few were bored, but fewer were truly happy.

Something needed to happen,

an adjustment needed to be made. Since the universe had already been created and humans already born, she couldn't put the trillions of pieces of herself back together, so another idea sprang forth from her limitless mind. Beaming with excitement at the simplicity of her new thought, God decided to send to the world once every hundred years a piece of herself with a good strong memory to remind everybody of who and what they really were. Not being particularly attached to being a woman she thought, "I will come as a man" And this she did. Once she was born as a prince in India and she called herself Buddha. And once she was born as a baby in Egypt. She called herself Moses and had herself floated down the Nile. And later she was born in a manger.

He was born humbly,

offering a hint to those enticed by the worlds riches and abundance that God's kingdom is beyond the world and better than riches. Those who remembered sought out the new-born, those who forgot stayed home. The child grew up quickly, and when he could speak, he did his best to remind people that they were made of a boundless imagination a complete intelligence, that they were God.

Because this young one had the memory of God, he knew how to use his imagination to create in an instant, anything he thought. If he wanted to feed his friends, he would think fish, and then more fish appeared than they could possibly eat. Those who were forgetful, which was almost everyone, were shocked by these actions, yet he patiently and lovingly showed them how they could create anything. "What I can do, you can do and more," he said. Most people did not believe this and claimed the young man to be a magician, a trickster. "Seek the kingdom of God inside you, then everything else will be added," he said.

"Surely they would understand."

God thought to herself, "surely they should know who they are, for they are me and I am them." But, sadly, the most forgetful ones, those fighting to own the world, found the young man threatening, and they arrested him and tied his body to a stake. Because he had the compassion of God he simply whispered to himself, "Forgive them for they know not what they are doing." He reminded himself not to be disheartened but to leave the world in Love.

Now back in the realm of the Absolute, he entered the gates of eternity completely unharmed just in time for a massive meeting in his honor. He was tired but uplifted. God had sent to earth many representatives over the years, and as Jesus walked to his seat some of his fellow messengers encircled him. There was Krishna, Buddha, and Mohammed, all smiling and joining arms. Then Moses ruffled his hair and gave him a big hug.

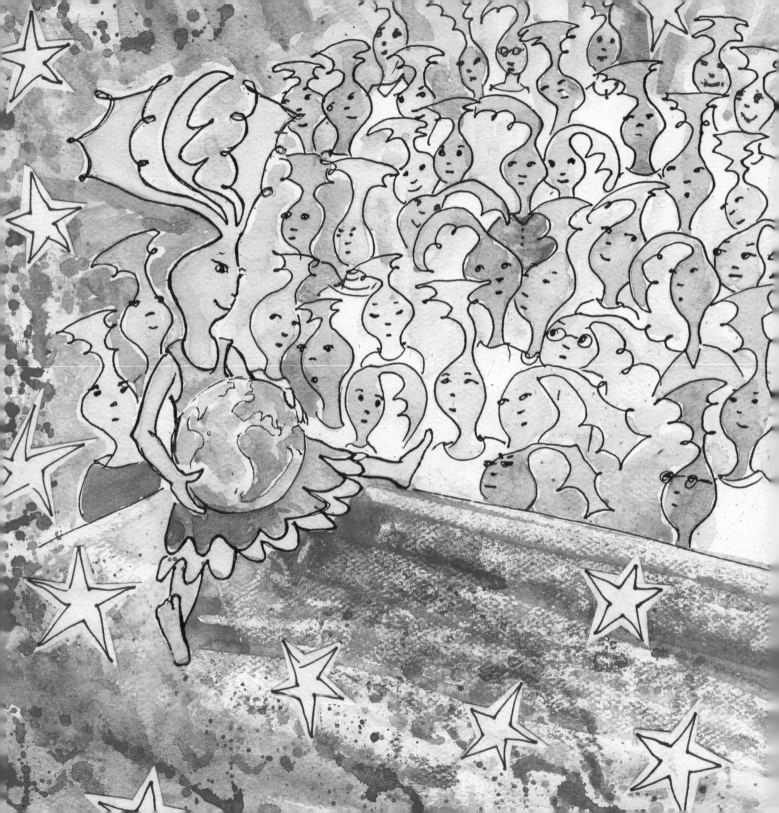

Smiling happily, Jesus sat down.

God had called together all the parts of her that had
returned to her boundless imagination, about 30 trillion
angels in all, to discuss this little problem on earth.

The problem was deeper than anyone suspected.

God reminded everyone that she had sent thousands of messengers, not just Jesus. Some fared pretty well, but now even those humans who heard the message and remembered were forgetting again and starting wars with different parts of herself. She opened the floor for discussion saying only that something radical had to happen, something revolutionary.

The discussion went on for a few hundred years.
Finally, there was a unanimous decision. It was decided
that God would go back to earth not with just a few
representatives but with an entire army. Not an army of
violence but an army of love.

God stood before the crowd
not sure if anyone would even want to go. "I will need
volunteers," she said. She expected only a handful, but
instead all 30 trillion beings put up their hands and a
euphoric roar reverberated though out the universe.

Unfortunately, the world couldn't handle
everyone all at once, so an eternal waiting list was started.
As all the angels scrambled to get in line, one angel stuck
up her hand and said, "God there's only one problem,
when we get to earth we will be forgetful like everybody
else. We will have forgotten all about this meeting. How
will you remind us? How will you make us remember?"

And God said,

"Brave little soul! That is a question for which I have a solution, so you must all listen very carefully. At an important moment in your earth-life, I will arrange for you to stumble upon a book. It will be called "A Little Story About the Biggest Thing That Ever Happened" and the instant you read it, you will remember everything and know it was you whom I sent." Smiling at God, the soul understood.

The End

About the Author

Will Dalton is a teacher and spiritual counselor who has taught hundreds of people around the world to meditate using the effortless, daily technique of Vedic Meditation. As a teenager in Australia, Will left school to crew racing yachts. By age twenty, he was an ambitious real-estate agent on the rise. He learned to meditate in order to conquer the business market—or so he thought. Will quickly fell in love with Eastern philosophy and his life soon took a different turn. For the last two decades, he has traveled the globe teaching yoga and Vedic meditation to all kinds of people, of every age, race, and creed. He wrote *A Little Story About The Biggest Thing That Ever Happened* as an exercise of the heart, to express all he has realized about the universal nature of spirit and the mechanics of creation, and to contemplate what happens when humans forget their essential nature.

He also wrote it for his two sons, Liam and Isa.

Acknowledgements

There are so many people to thank for this truly collaborative effort.

This list below mentions only a few:

My grandmother Joan who was my first spiritual guide.

Siimon Reynolds, for great leadership, friendship and generosity.

Annie Brunholzl, for discovering this gem of a book amongst a vast
quantity of other writing, and for coming up with the title.

Lisa Kaiser, who always makes me smile and for her delightful illustrations.

Justine Power, for her beautiful creative graphic layout of illustrations and text.

Thom Knoles, for teaching me almost everything I know.

Light Watkins, for being my brother from the other mother.

Basqaulie for two decades of humor and excellent coffee.

My Father, for his literary inspiration

My Mother, for her positive upbeat personality.

My two boys, Isa and Liam for simply being themselves.

And my deep gratitude goes to all other family members and friends
not included in this short list for their support and encouragement.

Lastly, I would like to thank Dominique Hackett for her perseverance and
drive in synthesizing all the design aspects of the little story so that you
can now be reading these words.

CPSIA information can be obtained
at www.ICGtesting.com
Printed in the USA
LVHW072100271221
707264LV00005B/98

* 9 7 8 0 6 1 5 3 8 6 3 8 6 *